Roselee Guinness is a young woman who is passionate about treating every person as an individual, regardless of disability. She had the privilege of meeting a young girl with a disability known as Rett syndrome. This inspired Roselee to write this book to allow other people to see that she is not so different, just special.

MY DOODLE IS A LITTLE DIFFERENT

ROSELEE GUINNESS

AUSTIN MACAULEY PUBLISHERS™
LONDON · CAMBRIDGE · NEW YORK · SHARJAH

A CIP catalogue record for this title is available from the British Library.

ISBN 9781528936897 (Paperback)
ISBN 9781528936903 (Hardback)
ISBN 9781528968881 (ePub e-book)

www.austinmacauley.com

First Published (2020)
Austin Macauley Publishers Ltd
25 Canada Square
Canary Wharf
London
E14 5LQ

This book is dedicated to Francesca Ross, who inspired me to look at life in a different way. Also to the amazing Rita, Gavin and Cameron for teaching me to become a better person and embracing me into the family.

I would like to say thank you to my beautiful mother, who taught me right from wrong but most importantly, she taught me how to read and write.
I would also like to thank the team at Austin Macauley for believing in my writing and wanting to publish my book.

Some people might say that my Doodle is a little different from the other boys and girls as she has a disability; the only difference I see, her smile is the most beautiful thing in the world, and you get lost in her eyes.

Other people don't take the time to understand my Doodle but never mind; their loss.
My sister Doodle has Rett
But this is why I am so happy we met
For she is not strange and weird
She is not to be feared.

People stop and stare all day
But they have nothing to say
Me and Doodle just smile and wave
I am proud that she is so brave.

My Doodle has wheels to help her walk.
My Doodle uses her eye gaze to
help her talk.

She may not have much speech
So therefore we need to reteach the world
That words are not always needed
To prove that my doodle has succeeded.

There are positives anyway
The blue badge I would take any day
Free parking, who wouldn't?
We take advantage of this, I know we shouldn't.

Just because Doodle is in a chair
Doesn't mean we can't do everything that we
love doing:
Swimming, horse-riding, going to the park.

Nothing stops us.

D stands for doing it! Doodle
The word Rett does not define my Doodle

She is just like you and me
And if Doodle is different
Then so are we.